all woman

VOLUME TWO

© International Music Publications Ltd
First published in 2000 by International Music Publications Ltd
International Music Publications Ltd is a Faber Music company
Bloomsbury House
74–77 Great Russell Street
London WC1B 3DA
Series Editor: Sadie Cook
Editorial, production and recording: Artemis Music Limited
Design and Production: Space DPS Limited
Printed in England by Caligraving Ltd
All rights reserved

ISBN10: 0-571-52831-7
EAN13: 978-0-571-52831-8

To buy Faber Music publications or to find out about the full range of titles available,
please contact your local music retailer or Faber Music sales enquiries:

Faber Music Ltd, Burnt Mill, Elizabeth Way, Harlow, CM20 2HX England
Tel: +44(0)1279 82 89 82   Fax: +44(0)1279 82 89 83
sales@fabermusic.com   fabermusicstore.com

all woman

VOLUME TWO

Anytime You Need A Friend

Words and Music by
Mariah Carey and Walter Afanasieff

Moderate ballad

If you're lone - ly
When the sha - dows

and need a friend
are clos - ing in

and trou - bles seem like
and your spi - rit

they ne - ver end,
di - mi - nish - ing,

Don't It Make
My Brown Eyes Blue

Words and Music by
Richard Leigh

Flashdance . . . What A Feeling

Words by Keith Forsey
Music by Irene Cara and Giorgio Moroder

16

I'll Stand By You

Words and Music by Billy Steinberg,
Tom Kelly and Chrissie Hynde

Oh, why you look so sad, the tears are in your eyes, come on and come to me now, and

Killing Me Softly With His Song

Tempo rubato

Words by Norman Gimbel
Music by Charles Fox

"Dreams"

Now here you go again

You say you want your freedom

Well who am I to keep you down

It's only right that you should

Play the way you feel it

But listen carefully to the sound

Of your loneliness

Like a heartbeat.. drives you mad

In the stillness of remembering what you had

And what you lost...

And what you had...

And what you lost

Thunder only happens when it's raining

Players only love you when they're playing

Say... Women... they will come and they will go

When the rain washes you clean... you'll know

Now here I go again, I see the crystal visions

I keep my visions to myself

It's only me

Who wants to wrap around your dreams and...

Have you any dreams you'd like to sell?

Dreams of loneliness...

Like a heartbeat... drives you mad...

In the stillness of remembering what you had...

And what you lost...

And what you had...

And what you lost

Thunder only happens when it's raining

Players only love you when they're playing

Say... Women... they will come and they will go

When the rain washes you clean... you'll know

Carol Carpenter
Close to You

Carol Carpenter
Close to You

One Moment In Time

Words and Music by
John Hammond and Albert Hammond

Pearl's A Singer

Words and Music by Ralph Dino,
Mike Sembello, Jerry Leiber and Mike Stoller

sing-er,___ she sings songs___ for the lost___ and the lone-
sing-er,___ and they say___ that she once___ cut a re -

- ly. Her job is en-ter-tain - ing folks,___ sing - ing
- cord. They played it for a week___ or so___ on the

songs and tell-ing jokes___ in a night - club.___ Pearl's a
lo-cal ra - di-o,_____ it ne-ver

(They Long To Be) Close To You

Words by Hal David
Music by Burt Bacharach

Moderato

Why do birds sud - den - ly ap -
why all the boys in

- pear ev - 'ry time you are near
town fol - low you all a - round

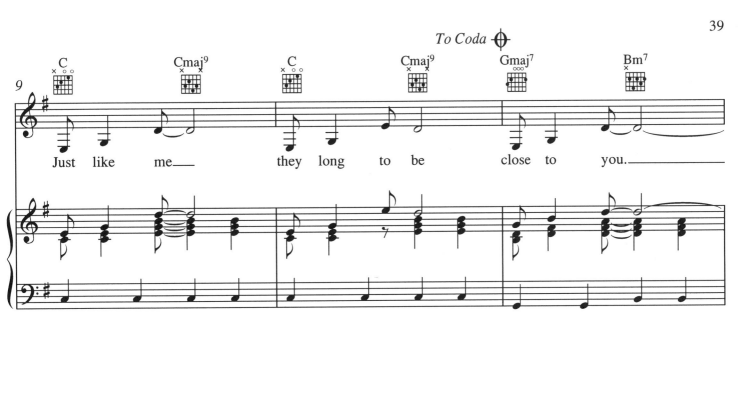

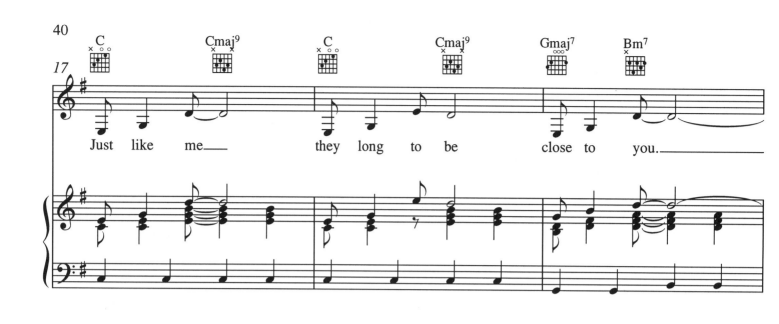

Think

Words and Music by
Ted White and Aretha Franklin

to make o-ther peo-ple lose their minds, well, be care-ful you don't lose yours, oh

CODA

You need me____ and I need you____ with-

-out each o- -ther, there ain't noth - in' ei - -ther can do. Oh,____

hey think a-bout me. (To the bone for deepness.)

Repeat and fade

True Blue

Words and Music by
Madonna Ciccone and Stephen Bray

Walk On By

Words by Hal David
Music by Burt Bacharach

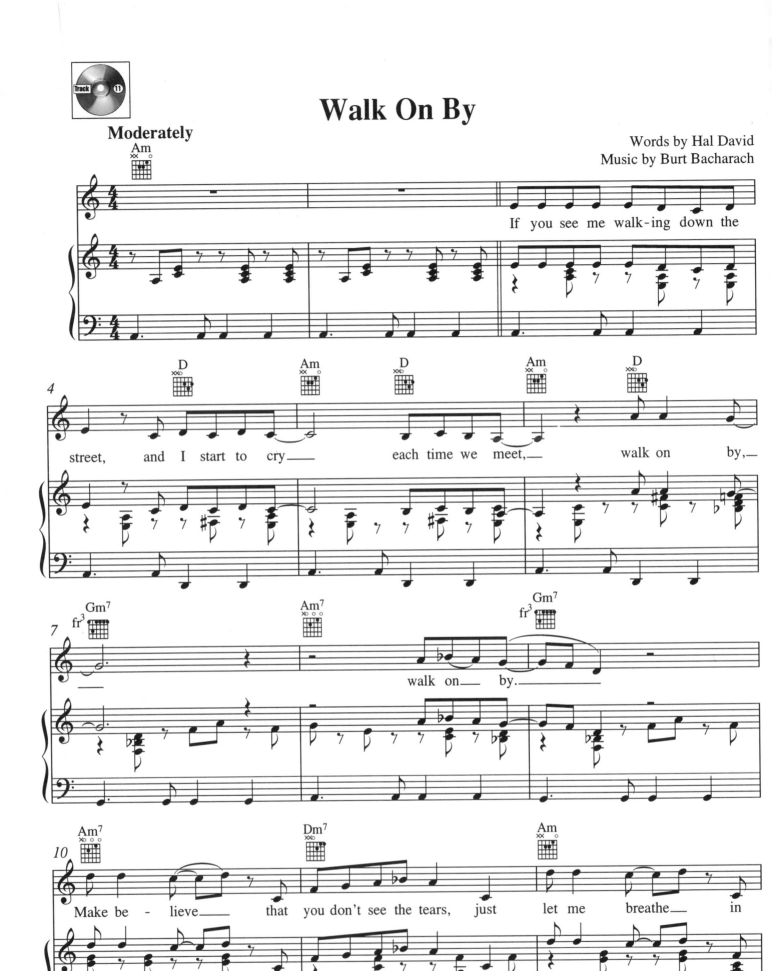

f you see me walking down the street + I start
o cry each time we meet — walk on by X 2

ake believe. That you don't see the tears just

+ me breathe — in private cos each time I see

on — I break down + cry — walk on by.

I just can't get over losing you. + ●

so if I seem broken in two — walk on by X2

Foolish pride — thats all that I have

left so let me hide — the tears + the ●

sadness that you gave me — when you

said goodbye —

If you see me walking down the street

+ I start to cry each time we meet

walk on by — w on by.

make believe, that you don't see the

tear, just let me breath.

In private cos each time I see you

I break down + cry ———>

walk on by

I just can't over losing you +

so if I seem broken in 2 — walk on by

Foolish pride — thats all that I have

left so let me hide the tears + the
sadness That you gave me when you said
goodbye

The Wind Beneath My Wings

Words and Music by
Larry Henley and Jeff Silbar

Slowly

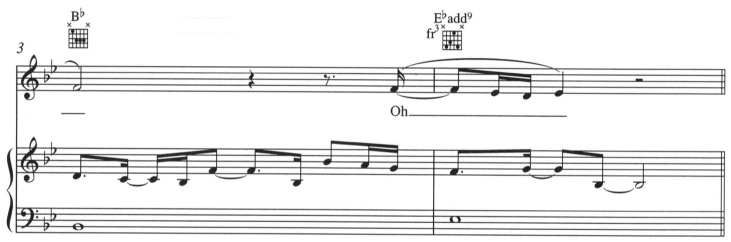

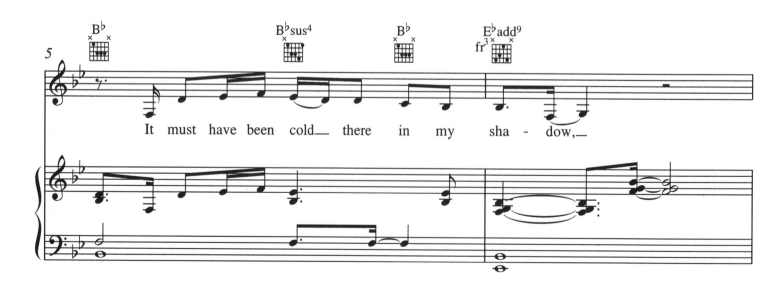

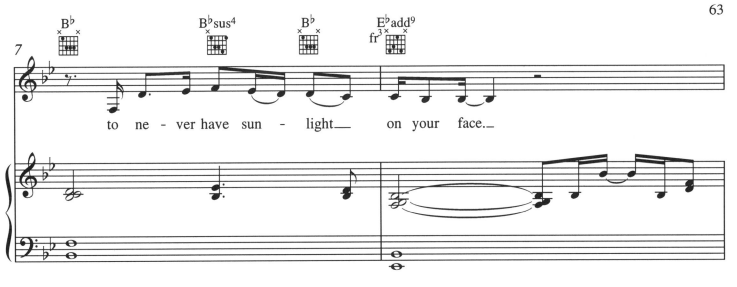

to ne - ver have sun - light__ on your face.__

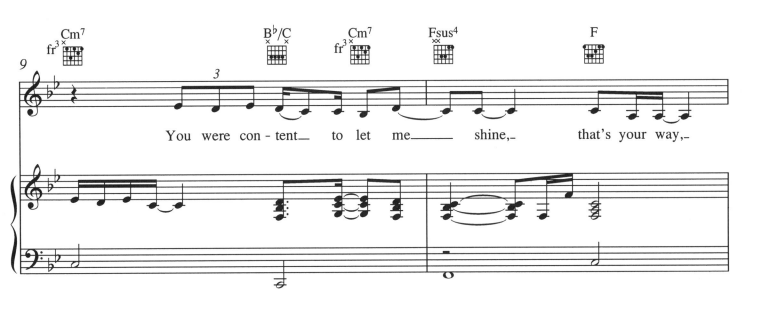

You were con - tent__ to let me___ shine,_ that's your way,_

you al - ways walked a step__ be - - hind.__

So I____ was the one with all____ the glo - ry,
It might have ap-peared to go____ un - no - ticed,

while you____ were the one with all____ the strength.
but I've____ got it all here in____ my heart.

A beau - ti - ful face with-out____ a name, for so long,____
I want__ you to know I know the truth, of course I know it,

You Don't Have
To Say You Love Me

Original Words by Vito Pallavicini
English Words by Vicki Wickham and Simon Napier-Bell
Music by Pino Donaggio

1-2-3

Words and Music by
Gloria Estefan and Enrique E Garcia

Bright dance tempo ♩ = 120

1. They tell me you're shy, boy, but I want you just the same.
2. Come out of your shell, boy, you know we go like hand in glove.
3. *Instrumental Solo ad lib.*

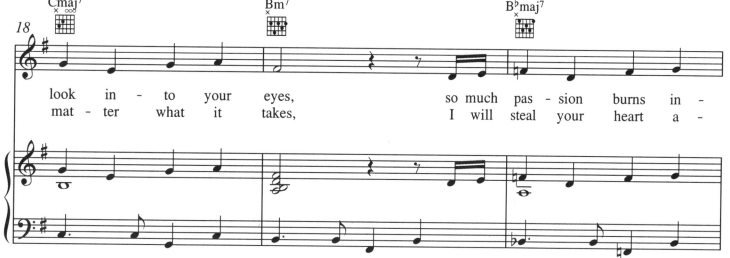

- side.   And if you need some coax - ing, I will— do it,
- way.   Take a chance for once, you won't re - gret it.

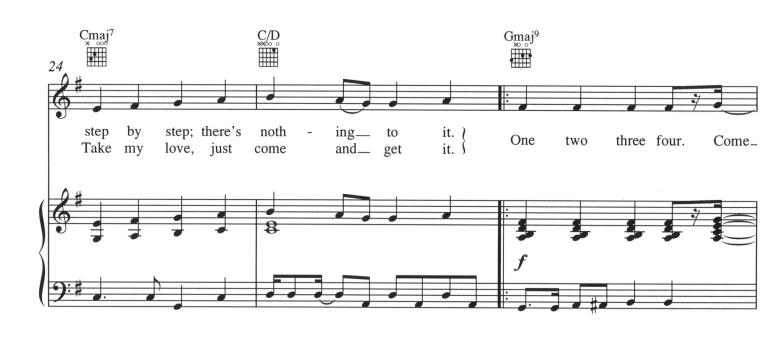

step by step; there's noth - ing— to it. One two three four. Come—
Take my love, just come and— get it.

— on ba - by, say— you love— me. Five six se - ven times.—

all woman

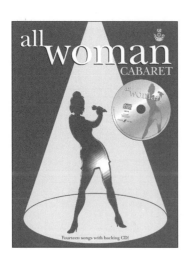

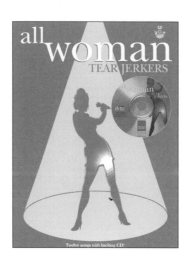

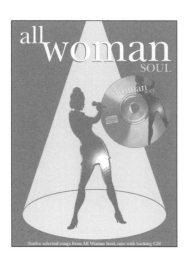

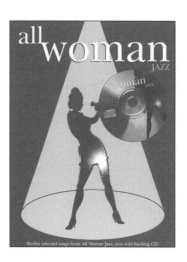

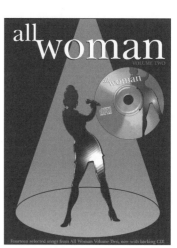

All Woman Collection. Vol.1 WITH CD

All Woman Collection. Vol.2 WITH CD

All Woman Collection. Vol.3 WITH CD

All Woman Collection. Vol.4 WITH CD

All Woman. Songbirds WITH CD

All Woman. Power Ballads WITH CD

All Woman. Love Songs WITH CD

All Woman. Jazz WITH CD

All Woman. Blues WITH CD

All Woman. Soul WITH CD

All Woman. Cabaret WITH CD

All Woman. Tearjerkers WITH CD

All Woman Bumper Collection WITH CDs

FABER ff MUSIC

To buy Faber Music publications or to find out about the full range of titles available
please contact your local music retailer or Faber Music sales enquiries:

Faber Music Ltd, Burnt Mill, Elizabeth Way, Harlow CM20 2HX
Tel: +44 (0) 1279 82 89 82   Fax: +44 (0) 1279 82 89 83
sales@fabermusic.com   fabermusicstore.com